20 Answers

&

End of Life Issues

Jason Negri

Catholic
Answers
Press

20 Answers: End of Life Issues
Jason Negri
© 2014 Catholic Answers

Published by Catholic Answers, Inc.
2020 Gillespie Way
El Cajon, California 92020
1-888-291-8000 orders
619-387-0042 fax
catholic.com

Printed in the United States of America

ISBN 978-1-938983-96-2
ISBN 978-1-938983-97-9 Kindle
ISBN 978-1-938983-98-6 ePub

Introduction

We don't like to think about death. Indeed, our culture has come a long way from the medieval monks who each day would offer one another the sober greeting, *Frater, momento mori*—"Brother, remember your death." Still less do we want to talk about "end-of-life issues." They're not subjects for polite conversation.

And yet death is the only certainty. Regardless of the worldly distractions with which we surround ourselves, regardless of our health, wealth, connections, or beliefs, regardless of whether we are ready for it, *all of us will someday pass from this life*. However unpleasant it may be, we ought to give this ultimate topic some attention—particularly at this moment in time, when controversies over euthanasia, physician-assisted suicide, and the rights of the sick and disabled have reached a crossroads.

That's what this booklet is for. It's a starting point, an introduction to certain end-of-life issues that many people haven't considered or just don't understand. It's written from a Catholic perspective but is not just for Catholics or even religious believers. Since death is the only certainty, these moral and ethical issues will impact us all. I hope that the information presented here will give you a better understanding of those issues, and of the principles that should guide us in navigating them. I also hope it will encourage you to have frank conversations with your loved ones about your end-of-life wishes and theirs.

1. What is the difference between euthanasia and assisted suicide?

It's always good to begin by defining our terms. *Euthanasia* means intentionally, knowingly, and directly acting to cause the death of another person—for example, giving him a lethal injection. *Assisted suicide* is defined as intentionally, knowingly, and directly providing the means by which another person commits suicide—such as giving him a prescription for a lethal dose of drugs. In both cases, the act is done ostensibly to relieve a patient's suffering. (Indeed, the word "euthanasia" comes from the Greek for "happy death.") The major distinction between assisted suicide and euthanasia is *who does the act*.

With euthanasia there is a further distinction: whether it is done with the patient's consent (voluntary) or without it (involuntary).

Euthanasia has been around since ancient times, when a patient may have been killed in order to end suffering that was unbearable and otherwise untreatable. In cases of acute suffering, such as when death was imminent and unavoidable, and there were no options for pain control, we can perhaps understand the motive for this practice.

In the modern era, though, advances in medical technology have enabled us to provide relief from acute pain, and even to improve many debilitating conditions that would have been completely untreatable centuries—or even decades—ago. Moreover, traditionally the purpose of medicine has been to preserve life, not to end it. The approach has been, "Cure, and if you cannot cure, care."

This approach has been violated in some high-profile cases, such as that of Jack "Dr. Death" Kevorkian, a Michigan pathologist who made a name for himself in the 1990s with his mobile suicide machine. His stated practice was to assist patients in ending their lives by hooking them up to his suicide machine, then having them flip a switch that sent poison into their system. He also practiced euthanasia, and was ultimately convicted of murder in 1999.

Such violations aside, in most of the civilized world, including the United States, both euthanasia and assisted suicide are illegal. In a few places, however, the legal status of assisted suicide has changed from a crime to a "medical treatment," and in others, voluntary euthanasia has become a legal and accepted way to end someone's life. We'll look at a few of these places later on.

2. Since suicide isn't against the law anymore, why should it be illegal to *help* someone commit suicide?

It's true that most countries no longer have anti-suicide laws on the books. But we shouldn't conclude from this that our society now thinks suicide is acceptable.

First of all, legality does not equal morality—in fact, history gives us many examples of things (for example, slavery) that were once legal but nonetheless gravely wrong.

Moreover, even though suicide is no longer illegal, our society still finds it tragic; it's just our view of it has evolved. Rather than seeing suicidal tendencies as a crime to be punished, we came to realize that they're often indicative of deep emotional pain, depression, or even a psychological disorder. Such a person needs help—not jail.

Evidence of this changed attitude can be seen in the increase of suicide-prevention programs, and the requirement in many jurisdictions for medical facilities to commit anyone whom they believe to be suicidal. Despite its legality, suicide is still something we as a people want to prevent.[1] Also, it should be remembered that there are over 30,000 suicides in America every year—far more than there are homicides. This problem is already very real, despite our efforts to prevent it.

In contrast to committing suicide, *assisting* suicide is not the act of a desperate or a sick person who needs help; rather it is done by someone with independent and presumably sound judgment—someone who should be helping to alleviate another's suffering, not helping that person kill himself. That is why, despite the decriminalization of suicide itself, assisting another's suicide remains and should remain a crime.

3. What about freedom of choice? If someone finds life intolerable, why shouldn't he be allowed to kill himself—even if it means getting someone to help?

From a Christian perspective, suicide is an offense against proper love of self, and an act that breaks the bonds of love and solidarity we have with family, friends, and God (see the *Catechism of the Catholic Church* 2281). Our lives are not our own; rather, they belong to God, and in justice we owe him stewardship of our life and health. Western cultures have traditionally drawn on this basic Christian ethic in opposing suicide.

But there is another reason why society should oppose suicide, a reason that has nothing to do with religious belief: Practically speaking, allowing suicide—and permitting others to assist in it—not only makes the act more acceptable, it allows it to become systematized. It's important to understand this reason and be able to communicate it, especially as our culture grows more secular and rejects religious foundations for its morality.

When we come to see physician-assisted suicide (PAS) as just another medical treatment, it will take on the legitimacy of any other medical treatment. Like other legitimate medical treatments, in certain circumstances it will be looked upon not as an option but an expectation—normal practice. As it becomes a normal practice, there will be pressure on vulnerable patients to choose it; just to get out of the way and stop being a burden. Proponents of PAS who swear that it will always be a purely voluntary option fail to account for the realities of human nature. The mere availability of PAS is a coercive force. It will never be limited to those who choose it voluntarily.

And what does this do to the practice of medicine itself? A profession whose very identity is to cure the sick and alleviate suffering would become complicit in causing death. As PAS becomes a routine solution, doctors who don't want to participate in it will have to defend their objections. Before long, physicians who refuse to participate in killing their patients might well face professional sanction for denying them that "right."

Finally, consider a person who is battling severe illness or pain. One day he may feel ready to give up, and the next day he may be prepared to fight on. This is part of the human condition. People in these circumstances, their strength of will ebbing and flowing, are vulnerable to suggestion and pressure. Giving them the legal equivalent of a loaded gun on a day when their will is weak—such as when they've just received a terminal diagnosis, or when their condition is particularly troubling, or before they've found a doctor who can give them the relief they need—is a very dangerous thing. Despair often comes in bouts, and can be caused by a number of factors, many of which are temporary. Is a choice to kill oneself under these loaded circumstances truly "free"?

4. Be reasonable! Some people are just lying there in a completely vegetative state. Shouldn't we just put them out of their misery?

Once again, let's define our terms, because there are different conditions that people mean when they say someone is "vegetative." *Persistent vegetative state* (PVS) is a term used to describe someone who is awake but unaware. The person has no apparent ability to understand or respond. Coma, on the other hand, is a sleeplike state from which the person cannot be wakened. Often these terms are used inaccurately.

A person in a coma or persistent vegetative state can't say he's thirsty. A person with either condition may be unable to express himself. Such individuals may not even understand what's happening. They'll simply feel thirst and inevitably will die of dehydration within five to twenty-one days. (It's often mistakenly said that such a person dies of starvation, when in fact dehydration occurs much earlier.)

By contrast, there is also something called "locked-in syndrome," in which the person is unable to move, respond to stimuli, or otherwise communicate, but is aware of what's going on around him. There have been many news stories recently about people in this condition who came out of it and recounted that they were fully aware of their surroundings. They could hear their loved ones talking about them as if they were already dead, and some talked about the horror they felt when they heard discussion of removing their food and water to "let them die."[2]

It is important to remember that, regardless of patients' mental state, they retain their dignity as human persons. And as such, they have a right to ordinary care, and certainly a right not to be directly killed! We might be tempted to think of them as less than human, and this might lead us to think it's okay to withhold ordinary care and so cause their death. But nobody should ever be denied food or water just because he can't communicate his needs and wishes.

5. What are some of the reasons that conscious and competent people give for wanting doctor-prescribed suicide?

This is an important question. If you listen to the rhetoric from those who advocate for the expansion of death-on-demand, you hear a lot about people suffering from unbearable pain, desperate for a way out. This tactic can be very persuasive, because no matter how cogent your reasons for opposing assisted suicide, they seem weaker in the face of a real person in real pain. Denying "relief" to such a suffering person can make you look heartless and cruel.

But the numbers tell quite a different story from the rhetoric. Reported statistics[3] from Oregon, where

PAS has been legal since 1997, reveal the following reasons given by patients for why they opted for death:

- Loss of autonomy (91.4%)
- Diminished ability to engage in activities making life enjoyable (88.9%)
- Loss of dignity (80.9%)
- Loss of control of bodily functions (50.3%)
- Burden on family, friends/caregivers (40.0%)
- Inadequate pain control or concern about it (23.7%)
- Financial implications of treatment (2.9%)

Note that "unbearable pain"—the most compelling reason offered by advocates of PAS—was *not* cited as the top reason on this list. In fact, the only reason even mentioning pain doesn't make the top five. And note how that concern is phrased: "Inadequate pain control *or concern about it*" (emphasis added). The "concern about it" part is critical, because it takes the issue of pain control outside the realm of actual experience and into speculation. *Fear* of untreatable pain is very significant in some people's minds (one out of every five respondents in Oregon). This fear does push them to consider suicide, but there is no way on this list of reasons of distinguishing the *experience* of actual untreated pain from the fear that it might happen.

But by far the biggest reasons have to do with autonomy, control, and dignity. This is hardly surprising, given the state of modern America.

We live in a very utilitarian culture, in which things—and people—are valued according to how useful they are. We also tend to be concerned with our self-image. So when we try to imagine not being able to do the simple things we enjoy now—or even perform basic functions such as walking or bathing—we tend to think, "I wouldn't want to live like that." Doctor-prescribed suicide can seem a legitimate option.

And yet it's very common for people who cavalierly swore in their impregnable youth that they'd rather die than lose their mobility or faculties to realize, when it actually happens to them, that they fiercely want to live. Humans have a remarkable ability to adapt to changing circumstances, and it's dangerous to base public policy, which affects everyone, on how we feel in the prime of our health, and how we *think we will feel* when we lose certain capabilities.

Finally, as the Oregon statistics show, some people also worry about becoming a burden to those they love, particularly a financial burden. Acting out of love and concern for their families, they might be prompted to request PAS to alleviate that burden. This is understandable, and to some degree it is normal. However, it should never get to the point of someone preferring death over a life that requires some dependency on others. Even if someone actually felt this way, it is hardly a compelling reason for us to support PAS, which

14

only legitimizes those feelings of being a burden. The takeaway lesson for the rest of us is that we should all be aware of whether our approach to caring for those in need is what is making them feel like a burden. When a loved one is in need, and becomes dependent on us, how are we responding? Are we helping joyfully, or are we feeding the "I'm a burden" mentality?

6. But what if a person *is* in unbearable pain?

Then this person needs all the help, compassion, and support we can give him! Our supporting his anguish-driven belief that life is not worth living would only worsen his suffering. Pain alleviation, or palliative care, has made tremendous strides in the past few decades, such that there are essentially no circumstances in which he should have to live in unmitigated pain. If a physician is not familiar enough with pain management to help his patient, it's time to find a specialist who is. In short, nobody in the modern world needs to suffer agony—certainly not to a point where death is seen as the only relief.[4]

Christianity offers an additional answer: the tradition of meritorious suffering, beginning with the belief in a God who became man, suffered, and died for the salvation of the world. Christ did not come to avoid suffering, or to take away ours. And suffer we will: Christ himself promised that those who follow him will take up their own crosses. It does no good to cling to a belief that God will take away all our sufferings if we just pray harder, love him more, or have enough faith. It doesn't work that way. This is a fallen world, and suffering, pain and, death are part of it.

But Jesus also showed that suffering can have value. We're able to unite our sufferings with those of Christ to bring about great spiritual—and perhaps even temporal—good. In Colossians 1:24, St. Paul talks about making up in his own flesh what is lacking in the sufferings of Christ. Even though Christ's suffering was perfect and lacked nothing, in some mystical way we're invited to participate in his salvific mission and offer to God our own imperfect sufferings.

And so, suffering can be an occasion of grace for us if we let it be, and not just for us who suffer, but for those around us who witness our faithful endurance.

For if we can bear our sufferings with patience and even perhaps with joy, we reveal to others the sublime truth that there can be value in suffering, and we can inspire others to greater holiness and virtue even as we are attaining it. Conversely, if we are perpetually complaining, saying "Why me?" and letting everyone around us know just how miserable we are all the time, it will not only take us down a spiral of despair and self-pity, but may injure the spirits and the faith of those around us.

We must bear in mind, however, that the Christian view of suffering does not mean that telling someone to "offer it up" is a sufficient response to his pain. First, such an admonition could too easily lead to resentment and despair. Not everyone is able to carry such a cross right away.

Moreover, even though suffering can be meritorious, Jesus nonetheless taught us to comfort those in pain. In the parable of the good Samaritan (Luke 10:25-37), for example, Christ didn't instruct his followers merely to offer spiritual exhortation to those in suffering; no, the praiseworthy Samaritan takes the man who was robbed, beaten, and left for dead on the highway and offers him material comfort and care. Likewise, in the parable of the sheep and goats (Matt. 25:31-46), those who attend to the physical needs of the suffering are rewarded in heaven. At first it may seem like a contradiction, but in Christianity suffering is both something to endure and something to ease. Faith in Christ and his example allows us to do the former. Medical science and Christian charity toward others can help us to do the latter.

The word "compassion" literally means "to suffer with," and it's not until we do this that we can offer those who suffer the help they need. This is true in all aspects of life, but particularly in end-of-life care, when the consequences of misguided compassion can be so dire. Those pushing for the legalization of assisted suicide try to claim the moral high ground of compassion for those who suffer. We cannot let them continue to do this by appearing indifferent to people's suffering. What can we do—what can *you* do—to help alleviate the pain of others? Can you point them in the direction of a doctor who understands pain and is certified in pain management? Can you bring them to a doctor's appointment? Can you help out around their house so their physical exertion is minimized? We have all become so consumed with the busyness of our own lives that we don't have time to bear one another's burdens.

7. What if someone is already dying? What's the problem with just speeding up the inevitable?

It is perhaps understandable that, when a patient is suffering and seemingly near death, his loved ones might want to shorten the time that he lingers before his final rest. It may seem like no harm is being done.

When you come right down to it, all of us are "already dying," aren't we? And most of us *would* have a problem with someone else "speeding up the process" for us!

So what does it mean, in this case, to be "already dying"? Is death imminent within hours or days? Or has the person just been given a terminal diagnosis? Such diagnoses are sometimes incorrect. Consider the case of one Jeanette Hall, who in 2000 was diagnosed with cancer and given six months to a year to live. She intended to use Oregon's assisted suicide law to ask her doctor to help her kill herself. (Indeed, she had voted in favor of that law in a 1994 referendum.) Her doctor, though, steered her away from suicide, and fourteen years later she is still alive and now speaking out against the danger of PAS.[5]

Even though Hall's case may not be typical of those with terminal diagnoses, it's not uncommon for patients to live longer than the time they're "given." And even for those who do not, their last weeks or months of life can still be a critically fruitful time of reflection and reconciliation, of setting things right in this world and preparing for the next. To tempt them away from that opportunity (since the mere availability of PAS tends to steer such patients, vulnerable to suggestions, toward choosing it) because they're "going to die anyway" is potentially to rob them of important moments they couldn't plan or predict.

None of this means that patients near death *must* try to extend their lives by every possible means. Later on we will look at the difference between *ordinary* and *extraordinary* means of preserving life, but for now it's enough to recognize that there's a difference between intentionally causing someone's death (for example, by smothering him with a pillow) and removing high-tech interventions that are preventing him from dying (for example, by disconnecting a respirator that is doing his breathing for him). In the first case, your intervention is homicide. In the second, you're allowing nature to take its course without extraordinary intervention.

8. Isn't your opposition to physician-assisted suicide based just on your religious beliefs?

Only if you think that protecting the weak and vulnerable is solely a religious proposition. Is it?

True, most major religions prohibit suicide (and thus assisted suicide) as gravely immoral. And the Catholic Church has spoken out especially clearly against assisted suicide and euthanasia. But this opposition is rooted not in some theological doctrine, but in the basic idea of human dignity, and respect for the value of life. You don't have to be a religious believer to agree with those things. Other good arguments against euthanasia and PAS are practical, based on what is good for us as a society.

Some of the most adamant opponents of PAS aren't motivated by religion at all—for example, members of the disability rights community. People with disabilities know what it's like to be seen as useless or undesirable or for their lives to be considered not worth living. They are concerned about the expansion of assisted suicide because they know that it is the disabled who are most at risk of being pressured into "choosing" it.

Doctors and nurses who work with the dying also tend to oppose assisted suicide. These people who care for the dying, who see their suffering daily, who work closely with them, are precisely the demographic that might be tempted to accept assisted suicide as a solution to the problems they encounter daily. But their experience with death and dying has taught them to see beyond what seems an expedient solution. They know that death can be an intense spiritual experience, even for those who don't claim any religious belief. And their work has taught them an important truth: You can't eliminate suffering by eliminating those who suffer.

We need to remember, too, that faith-based reasons for opposing PAS and euthanasia are not exotic dogmas but principles well grounded in the moral history of Western culture, shared and supported by Catholics, Christians, Jews, Muslims, people of other faiths or no faith. We're talking about helping—not hurting—people, and that message transcends sectarian differences.

9. PAS and euthanasia are already happening. So why not legalize them?

It's probably not a good idea to grant societal acceptance of something just because people are "doing it anyway." That's hardly a basis for good laws. With that rationale, we'd be legalizing every crime that already occurs.

But I think I understand what's behind this question. Those who are already assisting in suicides, or even euthanizing patients, are usually motivated by a misplaced compassion. They want the patients' suffering to end. From the intentional morphine overdose to the lethal injection, these practices have been around for as long as the medical profession itself. We know they happen. Sometimes people look the other way, sometimes there are consequences. But the motivation is usually honorable. Shouldn't we make a legal allowance for this already-occurring practice—if only to prevent its abuse?

Here we must first come back to the basics: It is always morally wrong to directly and intentionally kill an innocent human being. It would be dangerous and misguided to make a legal distinction for one type of murder because of hard cases or because we think we can regulate it.

We also must acknowledge the difference between legalizing a crime and choosing not to prosecute someone for it because of extenuating circumstances. This difference is very important from a societal point of view. A prosecutor may choose not to bring charges against a person who assists another's suicide because there isn't enough evidence or because the defendant's situation arouses so much sympathy that a conviction just isn't likely to happen. But at least the legal standard remains clearly articulated, and its protection of the vulnerable remains intact. In some cases there may be no practical way to achieve justice for every person who was given a lethal injection in his hospital bed, but upholding the legal standard will undoubtedly protect others at risk.

Some might say that we're better off legalizing PAS so that we can regulate it better—prevent it from being abused. This argument, however, fails on two levels: First, because it is no good solution to allow something that is wrong simply because people are going to do it anyway, and secondly because it fails to take human nature into account.

Look at it this way. Suppose there is increasing criminal activity in a particular neighborhood. The city council, frustrated with the police force's inability to deal with it, passes an ordinance stating that criminal activity in this neighborhood will only take place between 4 p.m. and 8 p.m. on weekdays. They have now permitted ("legalized") what was once considered to be criminal, for the purposes of being able to regulate (and presumably, minimize) it.

But does this really help anything? The activity is still taking place, and its negative effects, though "regulated" during the new hours, will still occur. Moreover, over time most criminals will be highly unlikely to limit their activities to the new permitted hours. Instead, it will push the boundaries of permissiveness. And so regulating the undesired behavior will not limit it but actually encourage it.

Remember that laws do more than allow us to punish crimes. They say things about our values; they teach.

Legalizing euthanasia or assisted suicide would teach that we as a society value radical autonomy more than we do the protection of the vulnerable—more than life itself. This is a very dangerous—and immoral—step for us to take, however much we may sympathize with those who can't bear to see their loved ones suffer.

Sadly, despite the broad prohibition of PAS, some caregivers are already hastening the death of patients in illicit ways: for example, administering medication such as morphine in amounts that far exceed that necessary to control pain.[6] This sad reality is only a taste of what would happen if we were to give legal approval to the practice.

10. The cost of medical care for the very old and ill can be a tremendous burden. Isn't PAS a solution?

Well, yes, but it's a pretty terrible one.

This question identifies one of the biggest problems with legalizing assisted suicide. As mentioned earlier, once the crime of doctor-prescribed suicide is transformed into an accepted medical treatment, it becomes just like any other medical treatment. Except with one huge difference: It's cheaper than any other medical treatment. As our culture struggles with the rising costs of health care, particularly the high costs of treatment at the end of life, it doesn't take much to convince people that the cheaper option is the *better* option.

In fact leaders in the movement to legalize prescribed death have been saying for years that economics, not the quest for individual liberties or increased autonomy, will drive assisted suicide to the plateau of acceptability.[7] Are we prepared to let this happen? Do we want to empower insurance companies—and now the government—to influence our end-of-life decisions by steering us toward death because it's best for their bottom line? Do we want medical decisions to be based not upon the patient's best interests, but on those of the family, the hospital, the insurance company, or the state?

It's also worth discussing *why* we're paying so much money at the end of life.

Until someone close to us actually dies, many of us don't think about our own mortality, and so we don't know how to face death when it comes. Even people who have serious illnesses often don't want to talk about it—with anyone—and so important conversations about the medical care they want (or don't want) never take place.

Fear about death and denial about its inevitability also lead many people to pursue every possible therapy and medical procedure that gives even a chance of living longer, without regard to the burden of the therapy (both in terms of financial cost and the possible burdensome side effects of the treatments themselves), or the quality of their life.

Studies about the cost of end-of-life medical care bear out these realities. A recent *60 Minutes* investigation found that just a few years ago, Medicare paid out $50 billion for doctor and hospital bills just during the last two months of patients' lives.[8] And it has been estimated that *20 to 30 percent of these medical expenditures may have had no meaningful impact.*[9] That's right, no meaningful impact, despite the very high financial cost.

It can seem crude to talk about money in comparison with human life. How much does one life cost? But in an age in which the rising cost of health care dominates our national discussion, and when resources are not limitless, the cost of care is relevant. What are we hoping to accomplish by pursuing every possible therapy, including those with serious side effects and little chance of success, in an attempt to live a little bit longer?

In his book *God in the Dock*, C.S. Lewis wrote, "I care far more how humanity lives than how long. Progress, for me, means increasing goodness and happiness of individual lives. For the species, as for each man, mere longevity seems to me a contemptible ideal." For those of us who really believe this life is not the end, why do we still cling to it at any cost?

In this context, we Christians find ourselves in perhaps an odd circumstance. We value life and have a duty to preserve it, but we have at the same time a broader perspective that allows us to recognize that this duty is not absolute, and that it is appropriate to draw a line and say "no more treatment," even if doing so will result in an earlier death. But whether from an excess of fear or hope, many people will pursue every possible treatment in an effort to live longer. And although this is not necessarily a bad thing, it behooves us all to pause and ask, "Why we are doing this?" Are we that afraid of our own mortality?

A strange twist on this is that advocates for PAS talk about how patients often exhaust all treatment options and are "kept alive" by a coercive medical establishment that has an economic incentive to continue prescribing treatments that realistically will not help. And only after "being tortured" by the medical field, the claim goes, do they realize that they are tired and they want to die *now*. And of course, it is our "duty" to help them. No one ever thinks to challenge their pursuit of treatments, even when they are extremely costly and come with debilitating side effects.

These facts must be faced and dealt with. Doctors and hospitals *should* tell patients what their treatment options are and what benefits and burdens they can reasonably expect to receive from these treatments.

Maybe if we as a society were more accepting of death, the drive to stay alive at all costs would not be so prevalent. Our failure to reckon with death and what lies beyond can create not just an economic cost but a personal cost. Increased discomfort, the debilitation and limitations that naturally come with age and infirmity, restrictions on diet, movement, and activities—these are things that we all must learn to accept as we grow older. It may be that we must also learn to accept that pursuing every possible medication, therapy, or treatment to extend our lives a little might not outweigh the collective burden such efforts place on us and our loved ones. We must reject the pro-PAS call for "death with dignity," but we'd be well served to approach death with *maturity*.

11. At what point should medical treatment be removed from a patient? Do I have to be kept alive by machines?

It would be a misrepresentation of Catholic teaching and good medical practice to say that we are morally obliged to "overtreat" patients—using every means available to sustain or prolong life. As we briefly saw in the previous question, in many circumstances life-sustaining medical treatment may indeed be discontinued, according to a prudential ethical analysis.

The U.S. bishops have written about this in their *Ethical and Religious Directives* guide to Catholic hospitals and health care providers. These ERDs are helpful and instructive for people looking for a solid set of ethical principles in this area.

Paragraph 56 states, "A person has a moral obligation to use ordinary or proportionate means of preserving his or her life. Proportionate means are those that in the judgment of the patient offer a reasonable hope of benefit and do not entail an excessive burden or impose excessive expense on the family or the community." The following paragraph provides a contrast to this: "A person may forgo extraordinary or disproportionate means of preserving life. Disproportionate means are those that in the patient's judgment do not offer a reasonable hope of benefit or entail an excessive burden, or impose excessive expense on the family or the community."

So we see that, far from insisting that everything possible be done to sustain a life, the Church's guidance shows us how to weigh prudently whether the benefit of a proposed treatment outweighs the burden it would impose.

Now, some people *do* take the position that there is a moral obligation to use any and all possible means to preserve and sustain life. This "vitalistic" perspective is permissible; someone would be within his rights to demand it for himself and indicate as much in his advance directives. But neither Catholic teaching nor traditional medical ethics makes this standard obligatory, and most people—acknowledging, perhaps, that at some point "enough is enough"— do not request it for themselves.

When considering a medical procedure or treatment in a particular circumstance, it's appropriate to weigh the expected benefit of the procedure or treatment against the burden it will impose on the patient.

(Note that we are considering the burden of the *treatment*, not the putative burden of the patient's life.) If the burden is deemed to outweigh the benefit, then the treatment can morally be forgone.

For example, if a proposed treatment is very expensive and has debilitating side effects, and the best that can reasonably be hoped for is that it will extend the patient's life by a few months (a chemotherapy protocol when the patient has advanced-stage cancer might fit this description), a person could choose not to pursue it.

And so a person may, in certain circumstances, refuse medical treatment for himself, or make that decision for another as his advocate or guardian. We are not required to pursue every possible medical option available, as if its burdens had no bearing on the decision. It's really a balancing test.

A similar test applies when determining whether to cease medical treatment for someone who is already dependent on it to live. Ordinarily, such treatment should be continued. But there are circumstances that might call for stopping it, circumstances to be evaluated according to the same kind of burden/benefit analysis used to determine whether to begin such treatment. How much is the procedure/treatment going to help? What burdens will it place upon the patient? This calculation must also include the fact that the patient is already undergoing the treatment and is dependent upon it for continued life.

When calculating the benefits of treatment, caution must be exercised to prevent falling into a "futile care" mentality that rejects any treatment that doesn't restore someone to robust health. This is not the appropriate standard by which to weigh a treatment's expected benefit, especially when the decision is being made by an insurance company or a government bureaucrat, whose incentive is to save money. Even the restoration to moderate health, for a very ill patient, should be recognized as a great benefit.

The state of medical technology must also be factored into the proportionality assessment. Treatment that might have been deemed "extraordinary" in the past might be quite routine today. For example, simple surgical procedures such as an appendectomy or kidney dialysis were once seen as extraordinary treatment options, but today are commonplace.

12. What about a feeding tube? Is there a different standard for deciding to withdraw that treatment?

Yes. The standard for removing a feeding tube generally is different from the standard used to determine whether life sustaining medical treatment should be discontinued. It is very common for people to conflate food and water provided intravenously or through a tube with life-sustaining medical treatment. In fact, just as your question implies, most hospitals consider "tube feeding" as "medical treatment." However, food and water—no matter how they are administered—are not medical treatment but ordinary, basic care and should be provided in all cases unless or until the body can no longer process them.

We need to think about what is actually being provided. Is it medicine, which cures a problem or provides therapeutic benefit? Or is it basic food and water, which every living thing—not just those who are ill—needs? The method of transmission is not essential—the aspirin you take orally to cure a headache is no more "food" than a can of liquid nutrition supplement is "medicine," whether it is taken orally or by a tube inserted into the stomach.

All human beings need four things to stay alive: warmth, hygiene, food, and water. Without any of these, any person will die, whether an Olympic athlete or an 87-year-old with Alzheimer's disease. Remove someone's warmth by leaving him outside in the Arctic Circle in January without a coat or a source of heat, and he will die rather quickly. Stay in the same position on the couch watching television for four weeks without moving (or being moved), and your pressure sores will fester and become infected, and you will die. Prevent anyone from eating, and he will die within six weeks. Prevent him from drinking, and he will die within three.

To point out that food and fluids are essential, ordinary care is not to say that they should *never* be removed. When death is truly imminent, the body begins to shut down. A person in that state will usually stop eating and drinking of his own volition. He simply isn't hungry or thirsty anymore. It serves nothing to force people to eat when their body is no longer assimilating the nutrition. It can actually make them uncomfortable. With this reality in mind, it is reasonable and ethical for a decision-maker to discontinue food and water on behalf of a dying patient when the patient is unable to communicate his own wishes. When the patient dies soon after, it is from his terminal medical condition, not from dehydration or starvation.

But it is, unfortunately, not an uncommon practice for patients in hospitals to die of dehydration. The horror of it is usually masked by morphine or other sedatives, but symptoms to look for include:

- Mouth dries out and becomes caked or coated with thick material.
- Lips become parched and cracked.
- Tongue swells and possibly cracks.
- Eyes recede back into their orbits.
- Cheeks become hollow.
- Lining of the nose cracks and causes the nose to bleed.
- Skin hangs loose on the body and becomes dry and scaly.
- Urine becomes highly concentrated, leading to burning of the bladder.

- Lining of the stomach dries out, causing dry heaves and vomiting.
- Body temperature becomes very high.
- Brain cells dry out, causing convulsions.
- Respiratory tract dries out, and the thick secretions that result possibly plug the lungs and cause death.

At some point within five days to three weeks, the person's major organs, including the lungs, heart, and brain, give out, and death occurs.[10] Death by dehydration is a horrible, horrible way to die. In no case is it ethically permissible as a means of "mercifully" ending a patient's life.[11]

It also bears mentioning that tube feeding is neither new nor expensive—in fact, it has been in use for more than one hundred years. Two articles, published in the 1896 *Transactions of the Kentucky Medical Society*, describe the ease with which feeding by gastrostomy tube (g-tube) was being accomplished at that time.[12] So in most advanced civilizations, there's nothing particularly burdensome or extraordinary about the use of a feeding tube.

13. I've heard the term "palliative care" in the context of end-of-life issues. What is it?

Palliative care is what a patient receives when his medical condition cannot be cured. Physicians have long subscribed to the historic principle that it is a doctor's role to cure, and when doctors cannot cure, they must care. The specialized field of palliative care recognizes that when medicine is no longer able to heal a patient, we can still provide him with relief from painful symptoms. The goal is to improve quality of life for both the patient and the family.

Palliative care is provided by a team of doctors, nurses, and specialists who work together with a patient's other doctors to provide an extra layer of support. It is appropriate at any age and at any stage in a serious illness and can be provided along with curative treatment.[13] The field of palliative care has grown in popularity, with the rise of the hospice movement and many hospitals adding palliative care specialists to their staffs.

As our society has become more technologically advanced, we sometimes forget that we can't cure everything. Some patients (or their families) have a hard time accepting the role that palliative care has to play in a course of treatment, feeling that choosing palliative care is tantamount to "giving up." The patient might refuse to accept his own mortality, but more often it is the family that has a hard time coming to grips with the reality of the situation. This can mean unnecessary delay in providing relief and is not fair to the patient. Palliative care, when approached correctly, can be a beautiful thing.

In some cases, palliative care can involve powerful medication such as morphine, sometimes in very high doses, to keep the patient's pain under control. It is an ongoing ethical discussion whether doctors might morally resort to palliative sedation to unconsciousness (PSU) (which involves continuously sedating the patient to a point of unconsciousness until death), where it is determined that any level of awareness causes the patient to experience pain. According to a recent survey, a large majority (85 percent) of physicians agreed that unconsciousness is an acceptable side effect of palliative sedation but should not be directly intended.[14]

Because morphine suppresses respiration, these efforts sometimes hasten the patient's death, so there was once some question as to the ethics of palliative sedation. However, this is resolved using a moral principle called *double effect*. According to the principle of double effect, it is morally permissible to perform an act that has both a good effect and a bad effect if all of the following conditions are met:

1. The act to be done must be morally good in itself or at least morally neutral.
2. The good effect must not be obtained by means of the bad effect.
3. The bad effect must not be intended for itself, but only permitted.

4. There must be a proportionately grave reason for permitting the bad effect.

So, applying this principle to the scenario of palliative sedation:

1. The act of providing pain-relieving medication is a morally good thing;
2. The good effect (pain relief) is not obtained by means of the bad effect (the death of the patient);
3. The bad effect (the patient's death) is not intended, but is permitted;
4. It's at least reasonable to hold that providing relief from severe pain is a proportionately grave reason for permitting the low possibility of the patient's death.

The principle of double effect can be discerned in the writings of St. Thomas Aquinas[15] where he talks about killing an unjust aggressor. This early formulation has been used by scholars, jurists, and doctors over the centuries to help decide difficult cases in an ethical manner. It is useful as a way to distinguish between palliative sedation and over-sedating the patient with a deliberate overdose of morphine, *intending* to bring about the patient's death. This is sometimes called "terminal sedation" and is the functional equivalent of murder.

Some people object that if you know a patient is likely—or certain—to die from the drug, that is the same as intending that death, but most theologians and ethicists disagree. If the intent is to relieve the pain, then a dose of medication adequate to the task may be ethically administered, even if that dose has the effect of suppressing the patient's respiration to a dangerous level.

Guided by the traditional understanding of the principle of double effect, palliative care can be a boon to those who are dying and to their loved ones. It takes a certain kind of person to work in this field, to offer service, care, and comfort to patients, and their work deserves better recognition. They facilitate the transition from life to death, helping the patient and his family accept the situation, and making his final days better.

It is worth noting that in polls, palliative care workers tend overwhelming to oppose the legalization of PAS. The very people who see suffering all the time and work to alleviate it are among those most opposed to allowing others to help patients kill themselves.

14. What is "elder abuse," and how does it factor into this debate?

Elder abuse has recently been a focus of mainstream media concern. It can take the form of physical abuse, sexual abuse, intimidation/psychological abuse, and financial abuse such as theft of the victim's assets (this happens all too often when an adult child is added on to the bank account of the victim and starts treating the victim's money as his own). Perhaps the most common form of elder abuse is neglect: Elders tied to chairs and left alone all day, given one meal per day, rarely or never bathed or toileted, ignored, left to languish. This often happens at the hands of their own children. According to the National Committee on the Prevention of Elder Abuse, some 4 to 6 percent of elders in America suffer some form of abuse. A 1996 study revealed that over 450,000 elderly experienced some form of abuse.[16]

We like to think that all older people enjoy a happy home environment where they are loved and cared for. The sad truth is that not everyone has this. As an attorney, far too often I see broken families where strife, mistrust, neglect, avarice, and outright malice are present. If your family is not like this, be thankful. But unfortunately, some are.

It doesn't take a very robust imagination to see how assisted suicide greases the skids to elder abuse. There will be pressure or even coercion from greedy heirs for elderly patients to die; vulnerable patients could be given the lethal drugs, masked by food or drink, and no one would know or even suspect what really happened; the abuser could make life so miserable for the victim that death would be seen as a welcome escape. The dysfunction already present in elder-abuse situations can too easily result in the victim's death, with the abuser getting away with it because there's no longer any evidence or someone to complain or testify.

It's easy for the general public to support the idea of assisted suicide when it's couched in terms of personal autonomy and rights—it's sometimes said that its supporters are "the white, worried, wealthy, and well." These people perhaps don't understand what it means to be marginalized, to be seen as having less worth or dignity than others, and they certainly don't know what it's like to live in fear. But it is a hard truth that there is already far too much elder abuse, and the availability of assisted suicide can too easily be used by unscrupulous family members to get rid of Mom or Dad much quicker, and hide their manipulations by making it all look like it was Mom's idea—Mom's *choice*—to go this way.

15. Is there anything I can do now to make sure *my* rights and wishes are respected in end-of-life situations?

Absolutely: You can—and should—execute a durable power of attorney for health care. This critically important document allows you to designate a trusted person to make medical decisions for you in the event you are unable to communicate your wishes regarding your own health care.

This document is a creature of state law, and the states have widely varying requirements. So it's a good idea to make sure that the document you execute complies with your state of residence. Either go to an attorney who specializes in this area, or contact the Patients Rights Council to get one of their state-specific Protective Medical Decisions Documents (PMDD). They have done the research to make sure that their documents comply with the state for which they are intended, and they keep abreast of changes in the law.

Please note that many states also recognize a document called a "living will," which purports to set down in advance the sort of medical care you do or do not want, in anticipation of a future event. Living wills are dangerous, as they literally give life or death decision-making power to an unknown physician. They provide a loophole big enough to drive a hearse through.

If your relative has a living will, you will not have any say in what happens if that person becomes incapacitated. Many people execute living wills thinking they are protecting themselves against being "kept alive indefinitely," but how it actually tends to play out is that the living will is used as a basis for hastening or affirmatively causing death, sometimes even in patients who might reasonably recover with a few weeks of artificially supplied assisted feeding or ventilation. The living will can provide a basis for a doctor or other health care provider to challenge any therapeutic measure wanted by a patient's family.

Decisions about appropriate medical care are best made by the patient (or made in the best interests of the patient by a trusted surrogate), and when they are made contemporaneous with the current medical diagnosis.

An attempt to determine medical treatment in advance without knowing the details of one's condition is hardly prudent and will be subject to misinterpretation. The totality of the circumstances needs to be fairly assessed, especially when trying to determine whether to discontinue life-sustaining medical treatment, and it's impossible to do this if the decision is being made beforehand.

It cannot be emphasized enough: Every competent adult, regardless of his state in life, should have a valid durable power of attorney for health care, naming a trusted individual to make medical decisions for him. Some people advocate putting end-of-life treatment guidelines in the document, to give some advice to your agents regarding your wishes (though it should be made clear that the directives are for your agent and *not* the medical staff, and that any discrepancies or uncertainties are to be resolved by your agent only), or you can just give blanket authority to your agent and not include any section of your wishes or guidelines, trusting your agent to assess the totality of the circumstances when/if the time comes and to make a prudent decision on your behalf.

16. I have heard about a new type of advance directive called a POLST. Is this a good idea?

No! POLST stands for Physician's Order for Life-Sustaining Treatment. Sometimes abbreviated differently in different jurisdictions (e.g., MOST, POST), the idea is the same—to institute an order regarding life-sustaining treatment that becomes part of the patient's permanent medical record. POLST is being promoted in many states as an efficient way for patients to communicate their wishes regarding medical treatment that may or may not be wanted. But there are problems with this approach.

How would a doctor know that the orders contained in a patient's POLST form are an accurate reflection of the patient's *current* wishes? More to the point, there is a concern that, depending on how the POLST is presented to the patient, it can make certain life-sustaining treatments—such as feeding tubes—seem unbearable, even though many people use them to live full and productive lives. The increasing acceptance of the POLST paradigm poses a threat to vulnerable patients who may well be susceptible to a coercive medical establishment or aggressive suggestions such as, "You don't really want to be kept alive by a machine, do you?"

Also, as the Catholic Medical Association has pointed out, POLSTs have patients make decisions about life-sustaining treatment beyond the context of their present situation, which could change. And with a POLST, the chosen surrogate or close family member is completely circumvented when it comes to decisions related to the patient's treatment options. These are both problems similar to those of the "living will," as we saw in the previous answer.

Finally, some states' POLST models do not even require a patient signature/sign-off, just the doctor's signature. Especially in jurisdictions with this practice, the POLST can be a dangerous option that results in patients' receiving treatment they do not want or not receiving treatment they *do* want.

Like a living will, the POLST approach sets out a standing medical order that may not apply to a patient's future condition, and it does so in a way that might be susceptible to abuse. It is a well-intentioned development, but it is more for the convenience of the medical community than for the real benefit of the patient. If a patient is concerned about "overtreatment" and "being brought back," he should realize that hospitals and medical facilities recognize the DNR (Do Not Resuscitate) order, and this should be sufficient to accommodate patient crisis situations.

17. What are the best arguments against PAS that both religious and non-religious people can agree on?

We've discussed some of them already, but here are a few of the strongest that, from our experience, are persuasive arguments for a lot of people:

1. *It cannot be limited to a voluntary choice. Its very availability pressures people into it.*

Those who support assisted suicide reassure us that it will only ever be for those who knowingly and competently choose it. They say that the safeguards in the law are working and that these practices will not expand beyond these "reasonable" boundaries. However, differing definitions make it difficult to even define the boundaries.

For example, the laws in Oregon and Washington define "terminal" as a condition that will, "within reasonable medical judgment, produce death within six months."[17] This "safeguard" has been challenged by some right-to-die advocates, who say that this prescribes a pointless time limit; that the longer the life expectancy, the greater the patient's suffering. And really, if you view it as a fundamental right to have assistance in ending your own life, when you choose and on your terms, there is no point in having a terminal diagnosis at all. Any such "safeguards" are an infringement on this fundamental right.

Also, the idea that euthanasia and assisted suicide should be practiced only if a patient has a terminal condition is not universal. In the Netherlands, for example, unbearable physical or mental suffering is enough to make one eligible for euthanasia.[18]

As for the idea that euthanasia and PAS will always be voluntary, it should be noted that their proponents wish to have them labeled "medical treatment." If one accepts this notion, then it would not only be inappropriate, but discriminatory, to deny death to a person solely because that person is too young or mentally incapacitated to request it. In the United States, a surrogate's decision is often treated, for legal purposes, as if the patient had made it. That means that, if euthanasia were legal, a court challenge could result in a finding that a surrogate may make a request for death on behalf of a child or an adult who doesn't have decision-making capacity. This is already happening in the Netherlands.

Even if surrogates were not permitted to choose death for patients, and if doctors did not end patients' lives without their request, there would inevitably be subtle—even unintended—pressure put on them. Such was the case with one elderly woman who died under Oregon's assisted suicide law.

Kate Cheney, 85, reportedly had been suffering from early stages of dementia. After she was diagnosed with cancer, her own physician declined to provide a lethal prescription for her. Counseling was sought to determine if she was capable of making health care decisions. A psychiatrist found that Mrs. Cheney was not eligible for assisted suicide since she was not explicitly pushing for it—her daughter seemed to be coaching her to do so—and she couldn't remember important names and details of even a recent hospital stay.

Mrs. Cheney was then taken to a psychologist, who said she was competent but possibly under the influence of her daughter, who was "somewhat coercive."

Finally, a managed care ethicist who was overseeing her case determined that she was qualified for assisted suicide, and the lethal drugs were prescribed.[19]

There is no doubt that the pressure for those with terminal illnesses to just "get out of the way" and to "stop being a burden" on the rest of us is already huge. If our society accepts doctor-prescribed suicide as a legitimate medical treatment, the pressure on already-vulnerable patients to choose it will only increase.

For those of us who might be faced with caring for loved ones who need our help, we need to be aware of the impact that even our demeanor can have on these dependent persons. Sometimes, unfortunately, our attitudes can increase their feelings of being a burden, and even contribute to depression. In extreme cases, this can lead to entertaining thoughts of euthanasia or doctor-prescribed suicide. But such thoughts are really cries for help. Beaten down by physical limitations or discomfort, shamed by dependence, and perhaps even depressive, those who depend on us might "choose" to end their lives. But how free is such a choice?

Those who are suffering need our support and assistance, not a guilt trip for being in need. Isn't it incumbent upon us to alleviate our loved ones' conditions, rather than offering them poison? We must take care not to feed—consciously or not—their feelings of being a burden. We must strive not only to help them bear their burdens, but to do so joyfully.

Certainly, caring for a dependent loved one can present great challenges, but almost everyone who has gone through this will tell you that the experience is also rewarding; they wouldn't have it any other way. As one woman told me: "Taking care of my parents was a privilege; it's also 'payback' in a sense for their raising me for eighteen years. My husband and I don't regret it. We were blessed to have them here, to pay them back a little for all they did for us."

As the Baby Boomers enter old age and more people find themselves taking care of elderly parents, many support services have arisen to help share the load. There are in-home living assistants to help with cleaning and cooking; home health care providers to administer medication, give regular checkups, and even help with bathing and toileting. For those unable to live at home any longer, assisted-living facilities or nursing-home care can be good, albeit expensive, options. Social services groups, such as Catholic Charities, also offer programs such as meal delivery or financial assistance to homebound elders.

People who don't want to face death—and the process of debilitation and illness that might lead up to it—are inclined to support anything that keeps it all neatly tied up, handled by "the experts" and out of the public eye. Doctor-assisted suicide? Why not? If someone wants to end it all, they ask, why should their doctor *not* be enlisted to help him? It's easier to have it all scheduled and done with, no? Avoid the messiness that will likely accompany it.

But it is in part the messiness that makes life what it is. It's our common humanity. And if we've lost sight of this, caught up in the rat race of trying to get ahead, we will almost certainly be contributing to the mentality that sees the dependent as nothing but a burden: and *that* is why the elderly, infirm, and disabled might consider killing themselves rather than being labeled "a burden."

Surely we as a society can do better than this.

2. *Doctor-prescribed suicide will be used as a means of cutting costs.*

This second argument is based on economic realities. As we have already discussed, when doctor-prescribed suicide is transformed into an accepted medical treatment, it becomes just like any other medical treatment, but with one huge difference: It's the cheapest option by far.

We're having an ongoing national discussion on health care that is driven by rising costs, particularly the high costs of treatment at the end of life. Already in Oregon, where death by prescription is an available "treatment," there are documented examples of patients who have been explicitly told that their health insurance will *not* cover the cost of their potentially life-saving or life-extending medication, but it *will* cover a prescription for suicide. This not-so-subtle message might be offensive to read here in this booklet, but it is positively devastating for someone with a serious medical condition to hear it from his insurance carrier.

This is why leaders in the "Death with Dignity" movement to legalize prescribed death have been saying for years that economics, not a love of individual freedom, will drive assisted suicide to the mainstream of acceptable practice. And they are correct. The "benefit vs. burden" analysis we discussed earlier can be appropriate to use when determining whether to start or to continue extraordinary treatment that might extend life, but it's a far cry from trying to justify killing a patient because treating him will cost too much. Yet this is exactly what is happening. If PAS is seen as a legitimate medical option, it not only can reduce the value of every life to a cost-benefit equation, but it will also encourage the likelihood that assisted suicide will be the preferred treatment.

Whether we're talking about a government-run health care system or a system of private insurers and providers, we should always ask: Do we trust those in charge to do the right thing, or the cheap thing? As costs keep increasing, it's not hard to see how some people might promote assisted suicide under the guise of "personal autonomy" when their real intention is to maximize profit.

3. *There is always the possibility of error in the diagnosis.*

The third reason is that, too often, the decision to die would be based on incomplete or erroneous information.

People make mistakes, including doctors. Many of us probably know people who lived for years after they were told they had a terminal illness, and we're grateful that they lived for so much longer. But on that day they received the terrible news, some of them might have wanted to end it all. Thankfully, the law prevented them from doing so. What if they'd had a doctor standing ready to prescribe death? What if family members had encouragingly nodded their understanding and assent, wanting to support them in their decision?

We can't afford to make a mistake regarding death. There's no reversing it. Ask the family of Pietro D'Amico, an Italian magistrate who, based upon an erroneous terminal diagnosis, travelled to an assisted suicide clinic in Switzerland in 2013 and killed himself.[20] Authorities are looking into the situation, and people are second-guessing themselves, but none of this will bring Pietro D'Amico back.

4. Assisted suicide provides the perfect cover for elder abuse.

At a time when incidents of elder abuse are already at record highs, the availability of PAS will only worsen the problem. Unscrupulous family members, perhaps already inflicting emotional and verbal abuse, will now be able to coerce their elderly relative into taking that last desperate step. Or perhaps pressure might persuade their victims to request the lethal prescription, even though they don't intend to take it, but when mom turns up dead because pentobarbital was mixed into her mashed potatoes, how would anyone know what really happened?

These are just some of the realities that tend to get overlooked in discussions of "death with dignity."

18. What is the legal status of assisted suicide in the United States right now?

As of this writing (early 2014), three jurisdictions have passed so-called "Death with Dignity" laws that have effectively transformed the crime of assisted suicide into a medical treatment: Oregon, Washington, and Vermont.

Oregon's Death with Dignity Act passed into law by voter referendum (51 to 49 percent) in 1994 but didn't go into effect until 1997. This made Oregon the first state to take this step. In addition to the overarching problem of legalized PAS, there are a number of specific concerns regarding the supposed safeguards written into the law:

- Oregon's assisted suicide law does not require that family members be notified when a doctor is going to help a loved one commit suicide.

- It permits doctors to help mentally ill or depressed patients commit suicide.
- It permits "shopping around" for a health professional who will find that a patient is qualified for assisted suicide.
- It allows the fatal dose of drugs to be mailed to patients.
- Requests for assisted suicide do not need to be made in person.
- It has no safeguards for the patient at the time the lethal drugs are taken.
- It gives doctors greater legal protection when they prescribe assisted suicide than when they provide pain relief and other end-of-life care to their patients.
- It does not preclude use of Kevorkian-like devices to induce death.[21]

These concerns undermine the claims made by supporters of the law that it has sufficient safeguards to prevent abuse or error, or to protect people with particular vulnerabilities, such as depression, from being victimized. They are the sort of issues that no one talked about when the proposal was being considered. Perhaps now, people who were convinced on principle that PAS is not a bad step for society might be swayed by particular examples of how PAS has played out in reality.

The supporters of Oregon's law worked tirelessly and poured millions of dollars into finding that all-important next state that would go in its direction. For years they tested the waters in numerous states, failing each time. They finally succeeded in the state of Washington, when Ballot Initiative 1000 (the Washington Death with Dignity Act) passed on November 4, 2008, by a vote of 58 percent to 42 percent. The Washington law is virtually identical to Oregon's assisted-suicide law.

With victories in two states, the advocates of death-on-demand were emboldened and ready to tackle other states where the demographics suggested they could win. On May 20, 2013, Vermont's Act 39 was signed into law, making it the first and only state to pass an assisted-suicide law through the legislative process.

On the judicial side, courts in both Montana and New Mexico have recently returned decisions that arguably permit doctor-prescribed suicide. In *Baxter v. Montana;* MT 449 (2009), the Montana Supreme Court ruled that rights granted under the state's living-will law form the basis for permitting physician "aid in dying," and that there is no legal prohibition against doctor-prescribed suicide. It remains an open question whether this actually permits the action or simply removes a legal penalty in certain circumstances.

And in 2014 a district judge ruled in the case *Morris v. New Mexico* that terminally ill patients who are mentally competent have a right under that state's constitution to seek a physician's assistance in ending their lives prematurely. Also, any doctor who provides this suicide assistance will not be prosecuted under the state's existing assisted-suicide law. This decision stands in stark contrast to the 1997 *Vacco v. Quill* decision of the U.S. Supreme Court, which determined in a unanimous opinion that a state's ban on assisted suicide did not violate the U.S. Constitution. The court in *Vacco* drew a clear distinction between a patient's refusing unwanted medical treatment and his requesting that a physician kill him.

American society is right on the edge of accepting this dangerous phenomenon, though the trend seems to be in our favor. National public opinion has been slowly turning against PAS, as this graphic shows:

Support for Doctor-Assisted "Suicide"

When a person has a disease that cannot be cured and is living in severe pain, do you think doctors should or should not be allowed by law to assist the patient to commit suicide if the patient requests it?

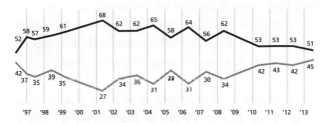

— % Should   — % Should not

Source: http://www.gallup.com/poll/162815/support-euthanasia-hinges-described.aspx

As the graph demonstrates, since 1997 American public opinion has been in favor of legalizing PAS (at least, in response to the way the poll question was phrased!). But in recent years, we see a trend building against it, with more people saying it should remain illegal, and fewer people saying it should be legalized and made available. Although this is encouraging, it demonstrates that we still have much more work to do.

Moreover, this graph gives results of a nationwide poll, but we have seen a very aggressive effort by the "death with dignity" lobby to tackle the issue on a state-by-state basis and weaken the laws that currently protect the vulnerable among us. They make an attempt in four to eight states every year, whether legislatively or by ballot initiative. Significant resources are put into the states that they have identified as demographically favorable to their cause—states with strong leanings toward individual liberties and autonomy, and that tend to be more politically progressive. And with every victory, they not only become more emboldened; they gain momentum in the eyes of their supporters (which helps in fundraising, because nothing succeeds like success), and they are that much stronger in the next state.

Although the U.S. Supreme Court in *Vacco v. Quill* rejected the idea that a state's ban on assisted suicide violated the Equal Protection Clause of the Constitution, the issue may well be revisited on a national scale when one of the current state proceedings is challenged in the federal courts. Laws change over time as society changes, and every victory for so-called death with dignity not only threatens the vulnerable in that state; it also represents another means to try to establish it as the law of the land.

19. What about euthanasia?

Euthanasia is not legal anywhere in the United States, but it is permitted in a few European countries. Inasmuch as these might be bellwethers for us—advocates of euthanasia and PAS like to point to Europe to support the reasonableness of their position—it is good to know what's happened in these countries.

The Netherlands was known worldwide for its practice of involuntary euthanasia even prior to its formal legalization there in 2002. Doctors who participated in the practice were simply not prosecuted, and the flouting of the law was so widespread that the Rotterdam Court in 1981 even issued guidelines for its practice. The 1991 *Remmelink Report*, a government-commissioned study[22] on the practice, found that in 1990 over 1,000 patients were killed by their doctors in cases of involuntary euthanasia—that is, doctors *killed their patients without the patients' knowledge or consent.* This practice has only increased in the years since.

In 2004, Eduard Verhagen, the medical director of the department of pediatrics at the University Medical

Center Groningen (UMCG) in Groningen, Netherlands, issued what has become known as *The Groningen Protocol*, which sets forth criteria for child euthanasia.[23] Obviously, these children cannot decide for themselves, so their parents and physicians are making the requests on their behalf. The acceptance of this practice among mainstream medicine in the Netherlands is a stark reminder of how societal acceptance of something leads to abuses and to the gradual acceptance of far more than was originally contemplated.

It is interesting to note that Dr. Els Borst, the former health minister and deputy prime minister who guided the law through the Dutch parliament, said in a 2009 interview that it was a mistake to proceed as they did.[24] Cases of euthanasia in the country have increased, and there are allegations of thousands of cases of involuntary euthanasia and dozens of killings of disabled newborns. Borst admitted that medical care for the terminally ill has declined since the law came into effect (at latest count, there are only two small hospices serving the terminally ill in the entire city of Amsterdam) and said that more should have been done legally to protect people who wanted to die natural deaths.[25] It is now estimated that one in every thirty deaths in Holland is from euthanasia.[26] This number is likely to increase with the institution of six mobile euthanasia teams: medical professionals dispatched in minivans to patients' homes, where the patients are too frail to move, or where the patients' requests for euthanasia have been denied by their primary physicians.[27]

The state of affairs in the Netherlands is particularly troubling, as that society stood firm against eugenics-based coercive euthanasia policies when they were occupied by the Third Reich during World War II.[28]

An example of the famous "slippery slope" in action, euthanasia was also legalized in Belgium in 2002. There exists today in Belgium a thriving market for organs harvested from euthanized patients,[29] despite serious ethical objections from many observers.[30] Belgium's euthanasia law was recently expanded again, in a 2014 decision to remove all age limits from the existing law so that children could be euthanized along with adults. There are certain alleged safeguards in the law, to avoid its being abused, but it is common knowledge that the safeguards are not observed. A 2010 report published by the *Canadian Medical Association Journal* revealed that in the Belgian region of Flanders, 32 percent of all euthanasia deaths were carried out without the patients' explicit request.[31]

Although euthanasia and assisted suicide are officially illegal in Switzerland, assisted suicide is penalized only if it is carried out "from selfish motives."[32] There is no prosecution if the person assisting a suicide successfully claims that he is acting unselfishly, resulting in a de facto legalization. There is no illusion in Switzerland that assisted suicide is a medical practice, so the person assisting a suicide need not be a medical professional to escape prosecution. Additionally, Switerland is known for Dignitas, an assisted-suicide clinic offering the terminally ill a chance to end it all in beautiful Geneva. They provide the poison, a rented hotel room, funeral and burial arrangements, and an emcee to run the operation, all for around $10,000. There are numerous stories of people traveling to Dignitas from all over Europe, despite Switzerland's protestations against "suicide tourism."[33]

What does Europe teach us? It teaches us that this monster cannot be contained: What starts as an option for some becomes an expectation for us all, resulting not only in pressure to commit suicide, but also in a change in medical standards and practice. Why should a society spend money on proper end-of-life palliative care when it is expected that people will just avail themselves of the quick and efficient solutions of euthanasia and assisted suicide? We also see how the actual practice of euthanasia and PAS will disregard safeguards placed into the law, to the point where some people in the Netherlands or Belgium carry wallet cards that explicitly say that they *do not want* to be euthanized—because they fear that the presumption now favors a lethal injection as the norm.[34]

There is no doubt that in this area Western civilization is rapidly unmooring itself from its Judeo-Christian roots. And in the name of individual autonomy and an inflated notion of personal rights, we are beginning to promote practices that threaten the very lives of the vulnerable among us. Catholics have the authoritative teaching of the Magisterium to help moor our principles and provide a spiritual and philosophical basis for our actions, and we must actively take those principles into the world, imitating Christ in serving the poor and weak, preventing them from being dragged to death, and standing for policies that preserve life and true dignity. Our challenge is to articulate these life-serving principles in ways that a post-Christian culture will understand and accept.

About the Patients Rights Council

The Patients Rights Council (PRC) is the oldest and largest nonprofit group that focuses exclusively on a patient's right to compassionate care, particularly at the end of life. The PRC's primary responsibility is to offer understanding and practical support to those who are facing critical situations for themselves or a loved one. We speak with people all the time about their medical issues and the problems they are facing with family members who don't understand, or people facing the denial of medical care that they need and want. We have found that there are some in our society whom we might call "the medically vulnerable"— meaning those people whose situations put them more at risk for the denial of proper and compassionate medical care. *We are a voice for these people.*

We work with patients and their families to make sure they are not denied medical care based on "futility" or *another* person's view of *their* quality of life. The PRC also provides up-to-date information on a range of end-of-life legal and medical issues, including medical power-of-attorney documents, doctor-prescribed suicide, euthanasia, futile-care policies, health care reform, and other related issues. PRC spokespersons also speak and write about the dangers that doctor-prescribed suicide and euthanasia pose to the medically vulnerable.

We also provide the public with well-documented facts about PAS and euthanasia. As we have seen, far too often our society tries to "solve the problem" of the ill and aged without giving consideration to the people threatened by their solution. So we educate people about what's behind the rhetoric of the so-called Death with Dignity movement.

The PRC builds and maintains strong networks with individuals and groups to influence policy and news coverage. As part of this networking, we provide assistance and training in the most effective ways to address particular audiences regarding doctor-prescribed suicide, euthanasia, and end-of-life issues.

To learn more about these issues or the mission of the PRC, visit www.patientsrightscouncil.org or call 740-282-3810.

20. What practical things should I be doing to prepare for my own death?

I'll suggest ten things:

1. Execute a durable power of attorney for finances or business.

This document goes by different names in different states, but the idea remains the same—you designate someone to handle your financial/business affairs for you in the event of your incapacitation. Executing one of these documents is much simpler and less expensive than conservatorship proceedings, and safer than just adding someone else's name to your accounts.

2. Execute a durable power of attorney for health care.

Naming a health care agent/proxy/patient advocate/decision-maker is of critical importance. You want to make sure you name someone you trust, who will make medical decisions on your behalf in the event you are unable to make them yourself. Also remember to:

• Name one agent at a time (to avoid split decisions), but name successors in case your primary-named agent cannot or will not act.

- Consult with an attorney who specializes in this area to help you craft your documents the way you want them.
- Include any particular instructions or limitations in these documents. *You* may know what you want, but the only way your agent—and others—will know is by putting it into writing.

3. *Avoid executing a living will or a POLST.*

These types of advance directives can be dangerous and easily subject to misinterpretation.

4. *Have the crucial conversation with your loved ones regarding end-of-life medical care and life-sustaining treatment.*

All too often, these conversations don't take place, and decision-makers may not have the guidance or reassurance they need to make certain judgment calls when the time comes. Do them and yourself a favor, and clearly communicate your wishes regarding these medical care issues. What sort of life-sustaining treatment do you want or not want?

5. *Think about becoming an organ donor.*

Pope St. John Paul II wrote in *Evangelium Vitae*: "[T]here is an everyday heroism, made up of gestures of sharing, big or small, which build up an authentic culture of life. A particularly praiseworthy example of such gestures is the donation of organs, performed in an ethically acceptable manner, with a view to offering a chance of health and even of life itself to the sick who sometimes have no other hope."

According to organdonor.gov, over 28,000 organ transplants were done last year alone. Generously giving up one's bodily organs to save or help another is laudable. Of course, since there is such a great need for organs— there are far more needy recipients on waiting lists than there are donors—care must be taken regarding the possibility of premature harvesting. If you wish to be an organ donor but have concerns about making sure your organs are harvested in an ethical manner, when you're truly good and dead (instead of harvesting being the *cause* of your death), then *don't* indicate organ donation wishes on your driver's license. Instead, make sure your proxy knows your wishes and has the authority to make that judgment call on your behalf only after assessing all the circumstances when and if the time comes.

6. *Execute a will.*

A basic will governs disposition of property, gives direction regarding funeral and burial wishes, and indicates custody of any minor children you may leave behind. If you don't create a will, you risk confusion and possibly some hurt feelings among your heirs, because their assumptions regarding these important matters might not be the same as yours or each other's.

In addition to a will, some people may also want or need a trust as a preferred vehicle to hold their assets and distribute them after death. Consult an estate planning attorney for guidance on whether your situation recommends a trust.

7. Consider your final bodily disposition.

Cremation or full-body burial? The Catholic position is one of preference for the latter, but cremation is permitted, provided it isn't done expressly to deny the resurrection of the body. Also, regardless of what someone chooses regarding final bodily disposition, the remains should be interred in blessed ground.

8. Get life insurance.

Particularly if you are the main breadwinner of a household, you should seriously consider life insurance to provide some income to your family in the event you are no longer around. Or, if you stay at home with young children, you should ask whether your surviving spouse will need to hire someone to replace the care you provide. Insurance can help with that expense as well. Finally, be mindful that even basic funeral and burial expenses can cost over $5,000. Even a minimal policy to cover these final expenses is a prudent idea.

9. *Make it easy on your heirs.*

You might have all your affairs in order (estate plan, financial statements, life insurance policies, pre-planned funeral and burial, etc.), and your system might make perfect sense to you, but will your loved ones be able to step in and easily assess and understand it? Do you have all your files in one place? An easy-to-read list of your assets with account numbers? If you have a safe in the house, will your heirs be able to access it?

10. *Write a letter to your loved ones.*

Last words of wisdom and love can be a powerful instrument for reconciliation and healing and will be something your heirs will treasure. You want to leave a lasting legacy? Write it to them.

About the Author

Jason Negri is the assistant director of the Patients Rights Council. Jason is an accomplished speaker and writer on estate planning and end-of-life medical ethics and is the co-author of *Freedom to Flourish: A Catholic Analysis of Assisted Suicide and Euthanasia*, published by the Knights of Columbus. He lives with his wife and children in Michigan, where he is a practicing attorney and an elected trustee of Hamburg Township.

Endnotes

1   The legalization of assisted suicide in states such as Oregon has
    resulted in a strange dichotomy: Police crisis negotiators have been
    taught to counsel suicidal people out of committing that desperate
    act, but they are also taught that, ultimately, a person has a right to
    "death with dignity." So the takeaway lesson is ... what? That suicide
    is a bad thing that we should try to prevent ... but not always?

2   http://www.dailymail.co.uk/femail/article-2019171/Dignitas-No-
    right-switch-human-life.html; http://www.worldmag.com/2005/03/
    don_t_let_me_starve.

3   http://public.health.oregon.gov/ProviderPartnerResources/
    EvaluationResearch/DeathwithDignityAct/Documents/year16.pdf.
    Realize that these numbers from the State of Oregon are only the
    reported numbers. There is no enforceable requirement imposed
    on health care providers to report information on patients who
    request and receive assisted suicide. Reporting is purely voluntary.
    This is important to note when the other side remarks on "how well
    it's working in Oregon" and how there are no complications. There
    are no complications because the only people reporting on such
    deaths are those who are complicit in it and have a vested interest in
    keeping it legal. It is unlikely we will *ever* hear of any complications
    regarding assisted suicide in Oregon.

4   It is beyond the scope of this booklet to treat fully the subject of
    pain control, but the Patients Rights Council (an organization that
    educates people about end-of-life issues) offers a book called *Power
    Over Pain*, co-authored by a lawyer and a doctor who is board-
    certified in pain medicine, to give practical guidance to both the

suffering patient and the doctor who treats him.

5   http://www.tcpalm.com/news/2010/oct/19/letter-im-so-glad-doctor-didnt-assist-me-with-of/.

6   http://www.nytimes.com/1997/07/23/us/when-morphine-fails-to-kill.html.

7   Derek Humphrey and Mary Clement, *Freedom to Die* (New York: St. Martin's Press, 1998), 313.

8   http://www.cbsnews.com/news/the-cost-of-dying/.

9   Ibid.

10 Brophy v. New England Sinai Hospital, no. 398, Mass. 417, 444 n.2, 497 N.E.2d 626, 641 n.2, 1986.

11 There is the rare case of a particular condition that makes the digestion of food and water excruciating, such as some types of advanced stomach cancer. In such cases, where the patient may not actually be in the dying process but cannot handle digestion, most ethicists agree that it is acceptable to withhold food and water, even if the patient dies thereby, provided the patient is aware of this and gives consent. As they say, though, "Hard cases make bad law," so this rare exception does not alter the general principle that sick people are not to be denied food and water.

12 L.S. McMurtry, "Modern Gastrostomy for Stricture of the Esophagus, with Report of a Case," and Coomes, "Gastrostomy, with Report of a Case," *Transactions of the Kentucky Medical Society* (1896).

13 http://www.getpalliativecare.org/whatis/.

14 Michael S. Putman, John D. Yoon, Kenneth A. Rasinski, and Farr A. Curlin, "Intentional Sedation to Unconsciousness at the End of Life: Findings from a National Physician Survey," *Journal of Pain and Symptom Management* 46, no. 3, 2013.

15 *Summa Theologica*, II–II, q. 64, art. 7.

16 See the NCPEA's website for more information: http://www.
preventelderabuse.org/.

17 Oregon Death with Dignity Act [ORS 127.800 §1.01 (12)] and
Washington Death with Dignity Act [Initiative 1000, § 1, (13)].

18 John Griffiths, Alex Bood, and Hellen Weyers, *Euthanasia and
Law in the Netherlands* (Amsterdam: Amsterdam University Press,
1998), 295.

19 Erin Barnett, "A Family Struggle: Is Mom Capable of Choosing to
Die?" *Oregonian*, October 17, 1999.

20 http://www.thelocal.ch/20130711/assisted-suicide-in-question-
after-botched-diagnosis.

21 The common perception is that a doctor would be involved in
writing a lethal prescription for the patient to orally self-administer.
But there is nothing that prevents another Jack Kevorkian from
creating a mobile death machine in a van and guiding a patient
through the process of injecting a needle and pushing a button to
get the poison coursing through his bloodstream. This image is
repulsive to many—especially that of a physician standing by to
help kill his patient—but it is a possible scenario under these laws.

22 *Medical Decisions About the End of Life, I. Report of the Committee
to Study the Medical Practice Concerning Euthanasia. II. The Study
for the Committee on Medical Practice Concerning Euthanasia* (2
vols.), The Hague, September 19, 1991.

23 http://www.patientsrightscouncil.org/site/euthanasia-assisted-
suicide-health-care-decisions/.

24 http://patient-data-vault.org/HVANewsletter/0120_Vol6No1_
2009Dec9_NowTheDutchTurnAgainstLegalisedMercyKilling.pdf.

25 Ibid.

26 http://alexschadenberg.blogspot.com/2013/09/netherlands-euthanasia-report-indicates.html.

27 http://www.dailymail.co.uk/news/article-2430479/One-thirty-deaths-Holland-euthanasia-choosing-end-lives-cancer.html.

28 Leo Alexander, "Medical Science Under Dictatorship," *New England Journal of Medicine* 241 (July 14, 1949), 45.

29 http://www.lifesitenews.com/blog/belgian-doctors-looking-for-disabled-patients-to-be-euthanized-donate-organ.

30 An excellent assessment of the practice of euthanasia in Belgium can be found in a 2012 report published by the European Institute on Bioethics, entitled "Euthanasia in Belgium: 10 Years On."

31 http://www.cmaj.ca/content/early/2010/05/17/cmaj.091876.full.pdf+html.

32 Article 115 of the Penal Code of Switzerland (emphasis added).

33 http://www.mirror.co.uk/news/uk-news/assisted-suicide-healthy-people-travelling-3164625.

34 Rita L. Marker, *Deadly Compassion—The Death of Ann Humphry and the Truth About Euthanasia* (New York: William Morrow and Company, 1993), 156.

Become part of the team.
Help support Catholic Answers.

Catholic Answers is an apostolate dedicated to serving Christ by bringing the fullness of Catholic truth to the world. We help good Catholics become better Catholics, bring former Catholics "home," and lead non-Catholics into the fullness of the Faith.

Catholic Answers neither asks for nor receives financial support from any diocese. The majority of its annual income is in the form of donations from individual supporters like you.

To make a donation by phone using your credit card, please speak with one of our customer service representatives at 888-291-8000.

To make a donation by check, please send a check payable to "Catholic Answers" to:

Catholic Answers
2020 Gillespie Way
El Cajon, CA 92020

To make a donation online, visit **catholic.com**.

TO EXPLAIN & DEFEND THE FAITH

catholic.com